Kindness:
A Vegetarian Poetry Anthology

Kindness: A Vegetarian Poetry Anthology
仁慈詩選

Published and translated by:
Rev. Heng Sure, Ph.D.
Buddhist Text Translation Society
1777 Murchison Drive
Burlingame, CA 94010-4504
www.drba.org

17 16 15 14   15 14 13 12 11 10 9 8 7 6
ISBN978-088139-880-9
Printed in Taiwan
Illustrated by: Shr Guo He
Design and layout by: Shr Heng Lung

Preface

by Rev. Heng Sure, Ph.D. Berkeley Buddhist Monastery
Chairperson, Buddhist Text Translation Society

For centuries, Chinese poets have written verses illustrating the Buddha's principles of kindness and compassion. The sentiments in the poems that follow have been collected and passed on through generations, memorized, illustrated and set to music. One reason for their continuing popularity is because they arise from kindness that touches the heart.

Now the poems have been translated into English, to touch the hearts of Western readers. It is significant that the authors of these poems were prime ministers, scholars, monks and nuns, farmers, aristocrats and men and women of letters, people from all walks who share a common thread: kindness that looks beyond satisfying a desire for flavor, to unselfish concern for the well-being of others. Each poem opens a

window onto a world where animals are souls who temporarily inhabit bodies different from ours, but who, like us, are moving towards enlightenment and liberation from suffering.

1

The Buddha taught that all creatures with consciousness, blood and breath are kin, members of a family connected in substance and in nature. Buddhists have always maintained that animals have feelings and that killing them causes unnecessary grief and suffering. Nobody suffers willingly; harm done to one hurts all alike. Chinese Buddhists incorporated the principle of kindness into the practice of meatless, cruelty-free eating. All creatures are family, and we don't eat our kin.

These poems arise from the insights of interdependence. The spiritual well-being of humanity on the earth is tied to the well-being of animals, as they are, in their fur and horns. Animals have a place at the table, not on the table. Seen this way, cows are not merely steak or burgers or veal; pigs are not just bacon or chops or ribs. Fish are more than fillets, chowder or seafood. Even the smallest of creatures deserves

 and receives respect; size is not the standard that determines their right to live; their right to live is a fundamental condition.

The poems reveal that an animal's body is more than simply meat; they show the soul, the inside as well as the outside. Looking  through the skin to the nature within the animal, we dignify our human stature. One who shares this insight inhabits a world rich in relationship, presence and vitality. Such a life is connected and related, not alienated, not broken or lonely.

Our editorial team invited a young Buddhist nun to illustrate these English translations. Her drawings emphasize children discovering the principles of kindness and compassion. A life's habits often begin during the tender, impressionable years of childhood, but a mind can change forever in the turning of the next thought. The poems in this volume arose in China but their insights are as universal as suffering and joy. We look forward to a day when Western poets and singers create verses and songs that celebrate our deeper connection with nature. May these simple verses lead to the profound insight that by establishing kinship with all creatures we become more truly human than before.

前言

釋恆實　佛學博士・佛經翻譯委員會主席

　　幾百年來，中國詩人寫下許多描寫佛教慈悲教義的詩詞，這些內容由文字、圖繪以及音樂代代相傳，這些內容之所以經得起時間的考驗，因為這都是最真摯的善念，可以觸動人心。

　　現在這些詩詞被翻譯成英文，一樣地觸動著西方人的心。值得注意的是，這些詩詞的作者涵蓋各行各業，大多是王公大臣、文人雅士、僧眾、農民、藝術家、識字百姓，他們都有著共同理念：超越一切欲望，不自私地關懷眾生。每一位詩人都為我們開啟了一扇拔苦得樂的窗戶。

佛陀教導我們，有意識、有氣血的眾生皆互為眷屬，在本性上都是同為一體的。佛教徒總是主張，動物是有感受的，殺生會造成牠們的傷痛與苦楚，無人願意受此苦楚，而這種的傷害看似單一卻是對全體眾生的傷害。中國佛教徒將這種慈悲的理念，融入生活中實行素食，不忍吃眾生肉，因為眾生皆互為眷屬，我們不吃自己的眷屬。

　　這些詩詞作者深深洞悉眾生間的相互關係，人類心靈的安康與動物的安康是息息相關的。眾生平等，因此動物絕非盤中殤，換而言之，牛絕不等於牛排、漢堡或者小牛肉。豬絕不等於培根、絞肉或者

排骨。魚類也絕不等於魚排、海鮮雜燴濃湯、或者海產食物。不論怎麼小的生物都應被平等地尊重，動物體積的大小無關乎生存的權利，生存是眾生的基本權力。

詩詞內容昭示動物的身軀絕非僅是血肉，而是和人一樣有靈魂。動物在皮毛之下和人類相同有高尚的精神。地球村的居民有著豐富的關係、風采與活力；生命是相互關聯的，並不孤獨、破碎或寂寞。

我們的編輯群邀請一位年輕的沙彌尼來描繪這些英譯漢詩，她

的畫著重於孩童對慈悲事物的表現；我們人一生的習性常養成於孩童時期的印象，而心思卻常因為不同的想法而有所改變。本書所收錄的詩詞源自中國，詩詞中洞悉著動物的悲與喜。我們期待有一天西方的詩人與歌者，能創作一些詩詞與歌曲來頌揚人類與自然的深切關係。但願這些簡單的詩詞，能深深啓笛我們與眾生的眷屬關係，讓我們越來越能發揮人性的光輝。

The Kind-hearted Hermit

-- Lu Fuhuang (Tang Dynasty)

Around this lonely mountain top myriad peaks revolve,
I've come to cultivate ascetic's disciplined resolve,
I take my broom and sweep away
the deer's tracks in the snow;
The deer passed by, but in the morning,
hunters will not know.

仁隱者

萬峰迴遠一峰深　　到此常修苦行心
自掃雪中歸鹿跡　　天明恐有獵人尋

—— 唐·陸甫皇

Song for Lovers of Fish

--Bai Juyi (Tang Dynasty)

I strolled at leisure by the pond,
To watch the fish afloat,
And met two youths with bait and rod,
In their fishing boat.
With different hearts
we take delight in watching perch and trout,
I have come to feed the fish,
they've come to hook them out.

愛魚詩

繞池閑走看魚遊　　正值兒童弄釣舟
一種愛魚心各異　　我來施食爾垂鈎

—— 唐 · 白居易

Watching Fish

-- Ou-yang Xiu (Song Dynasty)

The autumn water, crystal clear, reflects every hair,
The fish file slowly by, making ripples on the pond.
Startled by my shadow from the bank, they vanish;
And leap for the depths of the green lotuses.

觀魚

秋水澄澄見髮毛　錦鱗行慢水紋搖
岸邊人影驚還去　時向綠荷深處跳

——宋‧歐陽修

12

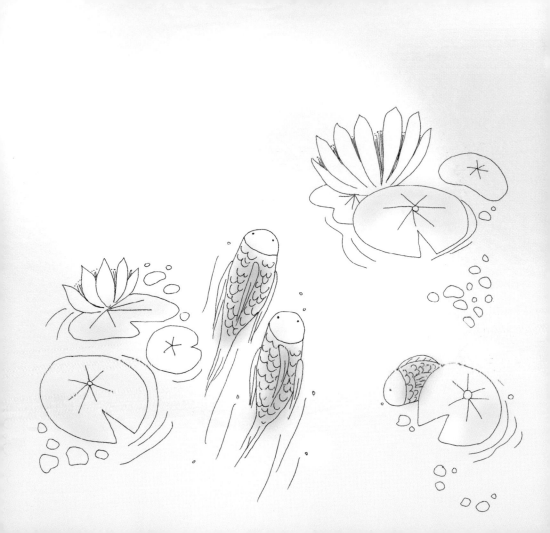

Girls Gathering Lotuses

-- Wang Shu (Qing Dynasty)

Lotus flowers and leaves fill the pond.
The blossom are fragrant, so is the water,
When the girls gather flowers, they don't pick them all;
They leave a few to shade the ducks
and drakes who live below.

采蓮詞

蓮華蓮葉滿池塘　不但花香水亦香
姊妹折時休折盡　留花幾朵護鴛鴦

──清・王淑

15

Starting Point of Compassion
-- Master Hong Yi (Republic of China)

Don't say that insects' lives don't count,
Don't say it's alright to let them drown.
Did you know that just one thought of compassion,
Is where basic human kindness begins?

仁之端

莫謂蟲命微　沉溺而不援
應知惻隱心　是為仁之端
———— 民·釋弘一

CAUTION
ANTS
X-ING!

17

On Protecting Life

--The Fool of Rong Lake (Qing Dynasty)

All creatures feel pain when they're hurt.
Even bugs and ants long to live.
Creatures' lives were given to them by Nature,
Tell the children not to take life lightly.

護生

萬物傷亡總痛情　雖然蟲蟻亦貪生
一般性命天生就　分付兒曹莫看輕

—— 清‧蓉湖愚者

An End to Hunting

--Du Fu (Tang Dynasty)

Spears and swords, weapons and shields,
The conflict never ceases;
Where are the phoenixes and unicorns of years past?
How can we enjoy hunting and call it sport?
Sages grieve when we waste the wealth of nature.

戒狩獵

天戈兵革鬥未止　鳳凰麒火受驚忡
臨刑遇赦恩無極　彼壽隆兮爾壽隆

—— 唐 · 杜甫

Geese

-- Lu Guimeng (Tang Dynasty)

The road from south to north stretches long,
Along the route myriad arrows fly,
Who knows, hidden by the clouds and mist,
How many geese arrive in Hengyang?

雁詩

南北路何長　中間萬弋張
不知煙霧裏　幾隻到衡陽

—— 唐·陸龜蒙

Final Goodbye

-- Master Hong Yi (Republic of China)

Taste the sorrow of parting from one's kin!
She turns her head around before she goes,
This time she won't return again;
Don't you wonder if her children know?

訣別辭

生離嘗惻惻　臨行復回首
此去不再還　念兒兒知否

——　民‧釋弘一

24

25

Poem on Stopping Killing

--Bai Juyi (Tang Dynasty)

The embrace of Nature gathers in alike
all creatures in water, land and air;
Imagine if you boiled in the cooking pot - -
The terror they feel would scald your bones, too!

戒殺詩

世間水陸與靈空　　總屬皇天懷抱中
試今設身游釜甑　　方知弱骨受驚忡

── 唐・白居易

Stop Killing!

--Chan Master Cloud of Vows (Song Dynasty)

For countless years the bitter stew
of hate goes boiling on.
Its vengeful broth is ocean deep, impossible to calm.
To learn the cause of all this conflict,
Terror, bombs and war,
Listen to the cries at midnight by the butcher's door.

戒殺詩

千百年來碗裏羹　冤深如海恨難平
欲知世上刀兵劫　但聽屠門夜半聲

—— 宋・願雲禪師

28

Stop the Slaughter!

-- Master Hong Yi (Republic of China)

The house is full of joy to the rafters,
Why add to it the grief of slaughter?
Your sole concern: the family's happiness;
Who cares about the animals' misery?

勸勿屠

喜氣溢門楣　如何慘殺戮
唯欲家人歡　那管畜生哭

————民·釋弘一

31

The Chinese Character "Meat"

-- Chan Master Hsuan Hua (1918-1995)

Within the word for meat two people reside;
The inner person pulls in the one outside.
When living beings consume each other,
Think it over, aren't we just like cannibals?

肉字

肉字裡邊兩個人　裡邊連著外邊人
眾生還吃眾生肉　仔細思量人吃人

—— 宣化禪師 （1918-1995）

Pity The Chicken

-- Yun Ju (Republic of China)

Roast chicken has been our dinner
for thousands of years;
To kill a hen you needn't use a butcher knife.
How sad that the poor chicken,
even with wings on her back
Can't soar aloft into the blue sky.

憐雞詩

千百年來席上肴　殺雞不必用牛刀
可憐背上生雙翅　不會高飛上碧霄

———— 民·雲居

Exhortation to Vegetarian Eating

-- Su Shi (Song Dynasty)

In autumn, frost and dew cover our eastern fields;
We harvest mustard greens and turnips galore,
My friend and I already ate our fill,
Why bring pain to chickens and pigs?

勸素食

秋來霜露滿東園　蘆菔生兒芥有孫
我與何曾同一飽　不知何苦食雞豚

──宋・蘇軾

37

Restrain Greed

-- Su Shi (Song Dynasty)

Will gluttony ever be satisfied?
Once food passes the throat, its gone.
Imagine instead, if we cherish blessings for the future?
Resting pure and tranquil: Ah! The happiness!

戒貪饕

口腹貪饕豈有窮　咽喉一過總成空
何如惜福留餘地　養得清虛樂在中

　　　　　　　——宋·蘇軾

The Joy of Home and Garden

-- Ye Tangfu (Ming Dynasty)

My home in the village on the river at sunset,
At the bend the current flows past my slat door,
I planted the pine tree
and now it's taller than the house,
I loaned it to the spring birds,
to raise their children and grandchildren.

田園樂

家住夕陽江上村　一灣流水遶柴門
種來松樹高於屋　借與春禽養子孫

——明‧葉唐夫

41

Enjoying Life

-- Bai Juyi (Tang Dynasty)

Heaven prefers life, it's true.
Every creature loves its life and wants to stay alive.
If we want to see our hundredth birthday,
Do not shorten the lifespan of others.

慶生

好生之德本乎天　物物貪生樂自全
我要長年千歲祝　不教物命一朝延

──唐・白居易

43

Encouraging Humane Kindness

-- Master Hong Yi (Republic of China)

Sentient beings despise cruel violence,
Yet all creatures love gentle kindness,
Even savage lions offer rides
To people who refuse to kill.

勸仁慈

眾生惡殘暴　萬物樂仁慈
不嗜殺人者　游山可跨獅

———民·釋弘一

44

Returning Birds

-- Master Hong Yi (Republic of China)

When the sun sets on the river,
Cooking smoke rises from the village homes,
Small birds return home, too,
Grateful for the kindness of their hosts.

歸鳥

夕日落江渚　炊煙起村墅
小鳥亦歸家　殷殷戀舊主
　　　　　　──民・釋弘一

47

On Liberating Life

-- Chan Master Shou Guang (Qing Dynasty)

He flew into the hunter's nets,
Trapped fast in mortal harm;
His painful end: the oven pot,
He trembled with alarm.
Condemned to die,
he won reprieve A kind act from a friend,
means His little life continues on,
And her lifespan extends.

放生詩

已赴網羅遭困厄　將投湯火受驚忡
臨刑遇赦恩無極　彼壽隆兮爾壽隆

——壽光禪師

48

49

May every living being,
Our minds as one and radiant with light.
Share the fruits of peace,
With hearts of goodness, luminous and bright.

普願諸衆生　心光常聚明
共享和平果　善念熾燃現

DRBA

An Introduction
to the Dharma Realm Buddhist Association

Founder: Venerable Master Hsuan Hua

Taking the Dharma Realm as its substance, DRBA
seeks to disseminate the true principles of Buddhism
to all areas f the world. Its missions are to translate
the Buddhist scriptures, to propagate the orthodox
Dharma, to promote ethics-based education, and to
benefit all sentient beings.

The guiding principles of DRBA are: no contention, no
greed, no seeking, no selfishness, no seeking of personal
advantage, and no lying.

In addition to the City of Ten Thousand Buddhas, DRBA has nearly thirty branch monasteries located throughout the United States, Canada, Asia, DRBA'S Sangha members honor the rules and practices established by the Buddha: eating only one meal a day, always wearing the precept sash, observing the precepts and being mindful of the Buddha, studying the teachings, practicing meditation, living together in harmony, and dedicating their lives to Buddhism.

DRBA'S institutions include the International Institute for the Translation of Buddhist Texts, the Institute for World Religions, the Sangha and Laity Training Programs, Dharma Realm Buddhist University, Developing Virtue Secondary School, and Instilling Goodness Elementary School.

The doors of DRBA's monasteries and institutions are open to anyone from any country who wishes to devote themselves to the pursuit of humaneness, justice, and ethics, and the discovery of their true mind.

法界佛教總會簡介

- 創辦人宣化上人。
- 以法界為體,將佛教的真實義理,傳播到世界各地為目的;以翻譯經典、弘揚正法、提倡道德教育、利樂一切有情為己任。

・以不爭、不貪、不求、不自私、不自利、不妄語為宗旨。

・有萬佛聖城等近三十座道場，遍佈美、亞洲；其僧眾均須恪遵佛制：日中一食、衣不離體，持戒念佛，習教參禪，和合共住，獻身佛教。

・有國際譯經學院、法界宗教研究院、僧伽居士訓練班、法界佛教大學、培德中學、育良小學等機構。

・本會道場、機構，門戶開放，凡各國各教人士，願致力於仁義道德、明心見性者，歡迎前來共同研習！

法界佛教總會 · 萬佛聖城
Dharma Realm Buddhist Association &
The City of Ten Thousand Buddhas
4951 Bodhi Way, Ukiah, CA 95482 U.S.A.
Tel: (707) 462-0939   Fax: (707)462-0949
www.drba.org / www.drbachinese.org
www.cttbusa.org / www.cttbchinese.org / www.bttsonline.org

國際譯經學院 **The International Translation Institute**
1777 Murchison Drive, Burlingame, CA 94010-4504 U.S.A.
Tel: (650) 692-5912   Fax: (650)692-5056

法界宗教研究院（柏克萊寺）
Institute for World Religions (Berkeley Buddhist Monastery)
2304 McKinley Avenue, Berkeley, CA 94703 U.S.A.
Tel: (510) 848-3440   Fax: (510)548-4551
www.berkeleymonastery.org

金山聖寺 **Gold Mountain Monastery**
800 Sacramento Street, San Francisco, CA 94108 U.S.A.
Tel: (415) 421-6117   Fax: (510)788-6001
www.goldmountainmonastery.org

金聖寺 **Gold Sage Monastery**
11455 Clayton Road, San Jose, CA 95127 U.S.A.
Tel: (408) 923-7243   Fax: (408)923-1064
www.drbagsm.org

法界聖城 **City of the Dharma Realm**
1029 West Capitol Avenue,
West Sacramento, CA 95691 U.S.A.
Tel: (916) 374-8268   Fax: (916)374-8234
www.cityofdharmarealm.org

長堤聖寺 **Long Beach Monastery**
3361 East Ocean Boulevard, Long Beach, CA 90803 U.S.A.
Tel/Fax: (562) 438-8902
www.longbeachmonastery.org

福祿壽聖寺 **Blessings, Prosperity & Longevity Monastery**
4140 Long Beach Boulevard, Long Beach, CA 90807 U.S.A.
Tel/Fax: (562) 595-4966

華嚴精舍 **Avatamsaka Vihara**
9601 Seven Locks Road, Bethesda, MD 20817-9997 U.S.A.
Tel/Fax: (301) 469-8300
www.avatamsakavihara.org

金峰聖寺 **Gold Summit Monastery**
233 1st Avenue West, Seattle, WA 98119 U.S.A.
Tel/Fax: (206) 284-6690
www.goldsummitmonastery.org

雪山寺 **Snow Mountain Monastery**
P.O. Box 272, 50924 Index-Galena Rd Index, WA 98256 U.S.A.
Tel: (360) 799-0699 Fax: (815) 346-9141

金佛聖寺 **Gold Buddha Monastery**
248 East 11th Avenue, Vancouver, B.C., V5T 2C3 Canada
Tel: (604) 709-0248 Fax: (604) 684-3754
www.gbm-online.com

華嚴聖寺 **Avatamsaka Monastery**
1009 4th Avenue, S.W. Calgary, AB, T2P 0K8, Canada
Tel: (403) 234-0644 Tel/Fax: (403) 263-0637
www.avatamsaka.ca

59

金岸法界 Gold Coast Dharma Realm
106 Bonogin Road, Mudgeeraba, Queensland 4213, Australia
Tel/Fax: (61) 7-5522-8788, 7-5522-7822
www.gcdr.org.au

法界佛教印經會（美國法界佛教總會駐華辦事處）
Dharma Realm Buddhist Books Distribution Society
臺灣省臺北市忠孝東路六段 85 號 11 樓
11th Floor, 85 Chung-hsiao E. Rd., Sec.6, Taipei 115, Taiwan, R.O.C.
Tel: (02) 2786-3022 Fax: (02) 2786-2674
www.drbataipei.org/ www.fajye.com.tw

法界聖寺 Dharma Realm Sagely Monastery
臺灣省高雄市六龜區興龍里東溪山莊 20 號
No. 20, Dong-si Shan-jhuang, Liou-guei Dist., Kaohsiung 844, Taiwan, R.O.C.
Tel: (07) 689-3713 Fax: (07) 689-3870
www.drbataipei.org/drm

彌陀聖寺 Amitabha Monastery
臺灣省花蓮縣壽豐鄉池南村富吉街 136 號
No. 136, Fu-ji-Street, Chih-nan Village, Shou-feng,
Hualien County 974, Taiwan, R.O.C.
Tel: (03) 865-1956 Fax: (03) 865-3426
www.drbataipei.org/am

佛教講堂 Buddhist Lecture Hall
香港跑馬地黃泥涌道 31 號 11 樓
31 Wong Nei Chong Rd., Top Floor, Happy Valley, Hong Kong, China
Tel: (852) 2572-7644 Fax: (852) 2572-2580

慈興禪寺 Cixing Monastery
香港大嶼山萬丈瀑
Lantou Island, Man Cheung Po, Hong Kong, China
Tel: (852) 985-5159

法界觀音聖寺（登彼岸）
Dharma Realm Guanyin Sagely Monastery
(Formerly Deng Bi An Temple)
161, Jalan Ampang, 50450 Kuala Lumpur, Malaysia
Tel: (03) 2164-8055 Fax: (03) 2163-7118

般若觀音聖寺（紫雲洞）
Prajna Guanyin Sagely Monastery
(Formerly Tze Yun Tung Temple)
Batu 5 1/2, Jalan Sungai Besi, Salak Selatan, 57100 Kuala Lumpur, West Malaysia
Tel: (03) 7982-6560 Fax: (03) 7980-1272

觀音聖寺 Guan Yin Sagely Monastery
No. 166A Jalan Temiang, 70200 Negeri Sembilan, West Malaysia
Tel/Fax: (06) 761-1988

馬來西亞法界佛教總會檳城分會
Malaysia Dharma Realm Buddhist Association Penang Branch
32-32C, Jalan Tan Sri Teh Ewe Lim, 11600 Jelutong, Penang, Malaysia
Tel: (04) 281-7728 Fax: (04) 281-7798

法緣聖寺 Fa Yuan Sagely Monastery
1, Jalan Utama, Taman Serdang Raya, 43300 Seri Kembangan, Selangor, Malaysia
Tel: (03) 8948-5688

發行人　法界佛教總會・佛經翻譯委員會・法界佛教大學
地　址　Dharma Realm Buddhist Association &
　　　　The City of Ten Thousand Buddhas（萬佛聖城）
　　　　4951 Bodhi Way, Ukiah, CA 95482 U.S.A.
　　　　Tel: (707) 462-0939　Fax: (707) 462-0949

出　版　法界佛教總會中文出版部
地　址　臺灣省臺北市忠孝東路六段85號11樓
　　　　電話: (02) 2786-3022　傳真: (02) 2786-2674

翻　譯　釋恆實
插　畫　釋果荷
設　計　釋恆瓏

倡　印　法界佛教印經會（美國法界佛教總會駐華辦事處）
　　　　地址 / 電話 : 同出版者
　　　　彌陀聖寺
　　　　臺灣省花蓮縣壽豐鄉池南村富吉街136號

出版日　西曆2014年 6月7日・初版六刷
　　　　佛曆3041年 5月10日・宣公上人涅槃日　恭印

www.drba.org / www.drbachinese.org